MIND TEASERS
LOGIC PUZZLES
& GAMES OF DEDUCTION

By George J. Summers

Illustrated by Arthur Friedman

Sterling Publishing Co., Inc.   New York
Distributed in the U.K. by Blandford Press

Fifth Printing, 1983
Copyright © 1977 by George J. Summers
Published by Sterling Publishing Co., Inc.
Two Park Avenue, New York, N.Y. 10016
Distributed in Australia by Oak Tree Press Co., Ltd.
P.O. Box K514 Haymarket, Sydney 2000, N.S.W.
Distributed in the United Kingdom by Blandford Press
Link House, West Street, Poole, Dorset BH15 1LL, England
Distributed in Canada by Oak Tree Press Ltd.
% Canadian Manda Group, P.O. Box 920, Station U
Toronto, Ontario, Canada M8Z 5P9
Manufactured in the United States of America
All rights reserved
Library of Congress Catalog Card No.: 77-79511
Sterling ISBN 0-8069-4566-4 Trade
4567-2 Library
8846-0 Paper

Contents

Introduction

The puzzles in this book have been composed to resemble short whodunits. Each puzzle contains some "clues" and it is up to the reader, as "detective," to determine from these "clues" which of the various "suspects" is the "culprit."

The general method for solving these puzzles is as follows:

The question presented at the end of each puzzle contains a condition that must be satisfied by the solution. For example, "Who does not stand guard with Ida?" contains the condition "does not stand guard with Ida."

The "clues," numbered when there are more than one, also contain conditions; these conditions concern the various "suspects." The "detective" must use all of the conditions to determine the unique "culprit" that satisfies the condition contained in the question.

Read each of the puzzles through carefully and try to find the best way to approach it. If you don't know where to start, turn the page and read the hints provided to set you on the right track. These hints are (a) a Solution Scheme, for the reader who needs help in relating the puzzle to its solution, and (b) an Orientation, where it is needed, for the reader who needs help in interpreting the "clues." In addition, each of the first two puzzles is accompanied by a Discussion on how to solve it.

Possibly the most useful section for learning to solve logic puzzles successfully is found in the Solutions section in the back of the book. As you complete a puzzle (or fail to answer it) and read the solution, follow the logical steps which were used to reach the conclusion provided. If you can follow the reasoning which eliminates the impossible choices until only the correct solution remains, then you will acquire the mastery needed to tackle any problem of logical deduction.

The Fight

Two of Anthony, Bernard, and Charles are fighting each other.

[1] The shorter of Anthony and Bernard is the older of the two fighters.

[2] The younger of Bernard and Charles is the shorter of the two fighters.

[3] The taller of Anthony and Charles is the younger of the two fighters.

Who is not fighting?

Solution Scheme and Discussion, page 8; Solution, page 92.

The Fight

Make a chart for yourself as follows:

Older fighter	Younger fighter	Taller fighter	Shorter fighter

Write "Anthony," "Bernard," or "Charles" in each box so that no condition is contradicted.

DISCUSSION

One could begin to solve this puzzle by making a table with headings as shown in the Solution Scheme and then by writing "A" (for Anthony), "B" (for Bernard), and "C" (for Charles) in as many ways as possible in the table like this:

Case	Older fighter	Younger fighter	Taller fighter	Shorter fighter
I	A	B	B	A
II	A	B	A	B
III	A	C	C	A
IV	A	C	A	C
V	B	A	A	B
VI	B	A	B	A
VII	B	C	C	B
VIII	B	C	B	C
IX	C	A	A	C
X	C	A	C	A
XI	C	B	B	C
XII	C	B	C	B

The next step would be to try to eliminate some cases using each of [1], [2], and [3] in turn: [1] explicitly eliminates cases II and VI, [2] explicitly eliminates cases VII and XI, and [3] explicitly eliminates cases IV and X. Now what? The person who is not fighting can still be either Anthony, Bernard, or Charles.

To get closer to the solution one must discover some *implied* conditions. From [1] it can be implied that Charles is not the older fighter, from [2] it can be implied that Anthony is not the shorter fighter, and from [3] it can be implied that Bernard is not the younger fighter. So [1] eliminates cases IX, X, XI, and XII; [2] eliminates cases I, III, VI, and X; and [3] eliminates cases I, II, XI, and XII.

So, from the earlier explicit conditions and the later implied conditions, the only remaining cases are V and VIII. Now what? The person who is not fighting can still be either Charles or Anthony.

To finally get to the solution, the relative heights of pairs of men can be compared from each of [1], [2], and [3] in turn for each of cases V and VIII. In one of these cases an impossible situation arises, namely, one man is both taller and shorter than another; so the case can be eliminated. From the one case remaining, the person who is not fighting can be determined.

The method just described is a tedious way to go about solving the puzzle because all the cases, twelve in number, are listed. Try to eliminate as many cases as possible before listing those remaining cases which involve more extended reasoning, but be careful that the list contains all those cases not yet eliminated.

See solution on page 92.

My Secret Word

One of the words listed below is my secret word.

AIM   DUE   MOD   OAT   TIE

With this list in front of you, if I were to tell you any one letter of my secret word, then you would be able to tell me the number of vowels in my secret word.

Which word is my secret word?

Orientation, Solution Scheme and Discussion, page 12; Solution, page 93.

The Tennis Players

Zita, her brother, her daughter, and her son are tennis players. As a game of doubles is about to begin:

[1] Zita's brother is directly across the net from her daughter.
[2] Her son is diagonally across the net from the worst player's sibling.

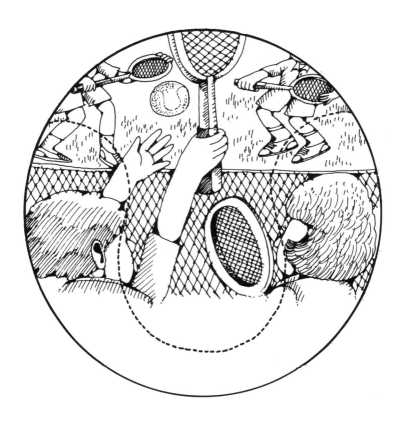

[3] The best player and the worst player are on the same side of the net.

Who is the best player?

Orientation and Solution
Scheme, page 13;
Solution, page 93.

My Secret Word

See solution on page 93.

ORIENTATION

"Any" in the second sentence enables you to determine my secret word.

SOLUTION SCHEME

Make a chart for yourself as follows:

A	D	E	I	M	O	T	U

Write "no" under each of the letters which cannot be in my secret word according to the condition given in the second sentence.

DISCUSSION

There are 256 possible ways that "no" could be written in the table. It is wise, then, to eliminate as many cases as possible, using the one "clue," before listing those remaining cases which involve more extended reasoning. Indeed, it turns out that only one case need be listed.

The Orientation tells the reader how to use the "clue." In other words, the "clue" says that *each* letter of my secret word is contained only in words having the same number of vowels. So M, for example, cannot be in my secret word because it is in AIM which has two vowels and in MOD which has only one vowel.

See solution on page 93.

The Tennis Players

Certain arrangements of four players on a tennis court are identical, though they appear to be different at first glance.

For example,   W | X   is identical to   Y | Z   because a rotation of one arrangement results in the other.

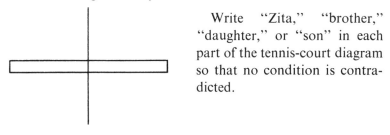

because a rotation of one arrangement results in the other.

SOLUTION SCHEME

Make a diagram for yourself as follows:

Write "Zita," "brother," "daughter," or "son" in each part of the tennis-court diagram so that no condition is contradicted.

After-Dinner Drink

Abigail, Bridget, and Claudia often eat dinner out.

[1] Each orders either coffee or tea after dinner.

[2] If Abigail orders coffee, then Bridget orders the drink that Claudia orders.

[3] If Bridget orders coffee, then Abigail orders the drink that Claudia doesn't order.

[4] If Claudia orders tea, then Abigail orders the drink that Bridget orders.

Who do you know always orders the same drink after dinner?

Orientation and Solution Scheme, page 16; Solution, page 94.

Equal Sums

```
A   B   C
        D
        E   F   G
                H
                I
```

Each of the digits 1, 2, 3, 4, 5, 6, 7, 8, and 9 is:

[1] Represented by a different letter in the figure above.

[2] Positioned in the figure above so that each of A+B+C, C+D+E, E+F+G, and G+H+I is equal to 13.

Which digit does E represent?

Orientation and Solution Scheme, page 17; Solution, page 95.

After-Dinner Drink

From "If X orders milk, then Y orders milk" and "X orders milk," the only possible conclusion is "Y orders milk." From "If X orders milk, then Y orders milk" and "Y orders milk," more than one conclusion is possible: either "X orders milk" or "X does not order milk."

SOLUTION SCHEME

Make a chart for yourself as follows:

Abigail orders	Bridget orders	Claudia orders

Write "coffee" or "tea" in each box in as many ways as possible—crossing off any unused boxes—so that no condition is contradicted.

Equal Sums

ORIENTATION

A, B, C, and D are respectively and simultaneously interchangeable with I, H, G, and F; only E can be determined with certainty. Each of A, B, D, F, H, and I occurs in only one sum; each of C, E, and G occurs in two sums.

SOLUTION SCHEME

Make a diagram for yourself as follows:

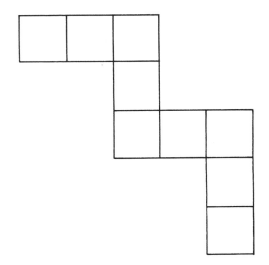

Write a digit in each box so that no condition is contradicted.

Relations

Lee, Dale, and Terry are related to each other.

[1] Among the three are Lee's legal spouse, Dale's sibling, and Terry's sister-in-law.

[2] Lee's legal spouse and Dale's sibling are of the same sex.

Who do you know is a married man?

Orientation and Solution Scheme, page 20; Solution, page 95.

X and O

The game of Tic-tac-toe is played in a large square divided into nine small squares.

[1] Each of two players in turn places his or her mark—usually X or O—in a small square.

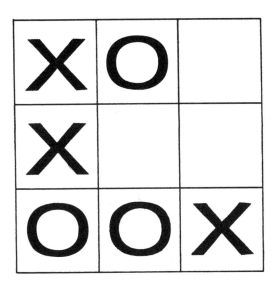

[2] The player who first gets three marks in a horizontal, vertical, or diagonal line wins.

[3] A player will always place his or her mark in a line that already contains (a) two of his or her own marks or (b) two of his or her opponent's marks—giving (a) priority over (b).

Only the last mark to be placed in the game shown above is not given.
Which mark—X or O—wins the game?

*Orientation and Solution Scheme, page 21;
Solution, page 96.*

Relations

ORIENTATION

A person's sister-in-law may be the sister of that person's spouse or the wife of that person's brother.

SOLUTION SCHEME

Make a chart for yourself as follows:

Lee's spouse
Sex M
       F
	Dale's sibling
	Sex M
	       F
		Terry's sister-in-law
		Sex M
		       F

Write "Lee," "Dale," or "Terry" in each box and indicate the sex of each person so that no condition is contradicted.

X and O

To determine which mark is the seventh mark to be placed in the game, you must determine which mark was the sixth mark placed in the game.

SOLUTION SCHEME

For convenience in discussing the puzzle, the squares can be numbered as follows:

1	2	3
4	5	6
7	8	9

Make a chart for yourself as follows:

The sixth mark placed in the game was in square number:	The seventh mark placed in the game was in square number:

Write the number of a square in each blank so that no condition is contradicted.

Hint: "1" in the first blank contradicts [3] because the X as a sixth mark would have been placed in square 5.

Names

Miss Alden, Miss Brent, Miss Clark, Miss Doyle, and Miss Evans have short first and middle names.

[1] Four of them have a first or middle name of Fay, three of them have a first or middle name of Gay, two of them have a first or middle name of Kay, and one of them has a first or middle name of May.

[2] Either Miss Alden and Miss Brent are both named Kay or Miss Clark and Miss Doyle are both named Kay.

[3] Of Miss Brent and Miss Clark, either both are named Gay or neither is named Gay.

[4] Miss Doyle and Miss Evans are not both named Fay.

Who is named May?

Solution Scheme, page 24 ;
Solution, page 97.

Hockey Scores

The Angoras, the Bobcats, and the Cougars are hockey teams. In three games the Angoras played against the Bobcats, the Bobcats played against the Cougars, and the Angoras played against the Cougars.

[1] The three final scores of the games consisted of the numbers 1, 2, 3, 4, 5, and 6.

[2] The difference between the Angoras' higher score and the Bobcats' higher score was one more than the difference between the Bobcats' lower score and the Cougars' lower score.

[3] The highest total of a team's two scores was achieved by the team that lost the greatest number of games.

Which team achieved the highest total of its two scores?

Solution Scheme, page 25;
Solution, page 98.

Names

Make a chart for yourself as follows:

Alden	Brent	Clark	Doyle	Evans

Write "Fay," "Gay," "Kay," or "May" in each box so that no condition is contradicted.

Hockey Scores

Make a chart for yourself as follows:

Angoras versus Bobcats	

Angoras versus Cougars	

Bobcats versus Cougars	

Write "1," "2," "3," "4," "5," or "6" in each box so that no condition is contradicted.

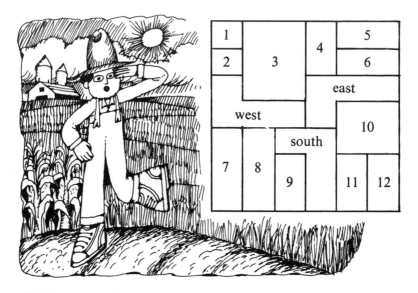

The Journey

The plan above shows an arrangement of corn, wheat, and rye fields. Jack is in the middle of one of the fields and has to meet his father in the middle of another field. On his journey from the field he is in to the field his father is in:

[1] His route takes him continuously through each of five other fields exactly once.

[2] He (being allergic to rye) avoids going through any part of a rye field.

[3] He notices no two fields of the same kind border on each other.

Which L-shaped field—east, west, or south—is a rye field?

Orientation and Solution Scheme, page 28; Solution, page 98.

The Visits

Alma, Bess, Cleo, and Dina visited Edna on Saturday.

[1] The time of each visit was as follows:

Alma at 8 o'clock,
Bess at 9 o'clock,
Cleo at 10 o'clock, and
Dina at 11 o'clock.

[2] At least one woman visited Edna between Alma and Bess.

[3] Alma did not visit Edna before both Cleo and Dina.

[4] Cleo did not visit Edna between Bess and Dina.

Who visited Edna last?

Orientation and Solution Scheme, page 29; Solution, page 99.

The Journey

The total number of fields involved in Jack's journey is seven.

SOLUTION SCHEME

Make a diagram for yourself as follows:

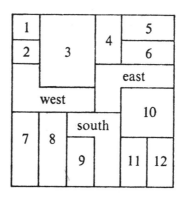

Assign each field to one of three arbitrary groups by marking like fields with one of three symbols. Find a route involving seven fields and marked with only two kinds of symbols.

The Visits

Each time mentioned may be either A.M. or P.M.

SOLUTION SCHEME

Make a chart for yourself as follows:

Order of visits				
Visiting times				

Write "Alma," "Bess," "Cleo," and "Dina" in some order along the top of the chart and the corresponding visiting times—"8," "9," "10," and "11"—below so that no condition is contradicted.

A Different Age

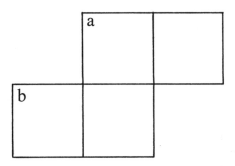

The ages of Ambrose, Brandon, and Chester can be related to the diagram above so that when just one digit is written in each box:

[1] a across is Ambrose's age in years.

[2] a down is the sum of Ambrose's age and Brandon's age in years.

[3] b across is the sum of Ambrose's age, Brandon's age, and Chester's age in years.

[4] Two of Ambrose, Brandon, and Chester are the same age in years.

Who is a different age in years from the other two?

Orientation and Solution Scheme, page 32;
Solution, page 100.

The Doctor and the Lawyer

One of Mr. Horton, his wife, their son, and Mr. Horton's mother is a doctor and another is a lawyer.

[1] If the doctor is younger than the lawyer, then the doctor and the lawyer are not blood relatives.

[2] If the doctor is a woman, then the doctor and the lawyer are blood relatives.

[3] If the lawyer is a man, then the doctor is a man.

Whose occupation do you know?

Orientation and Solution
Scheme, page 33;
Solution, page 101.

A Different Age

The diagram is read like a standard crossword puzzle. There are many ways to complete the diagram.

SOLUTION SCHEME

Make a diagram for yourself as follows:

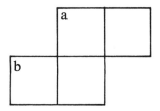

Write one digit in each box so that no condition is contradicted.

The Doctor and the Lawyer

ORIENTATION

In each numbered true statement:

Any assumption (an *if* part of a statement) that makes a conclusion (a *then* part of a statement) false must be a false assumption; any assumption that does not make a conclusion false may be true or false. "Doctor" and "lawyer" are placeholders for two unknown people; when a conclusion becomes false after substituting an ordered pair of people for "doctor" and "lawyer," the ordered pair must be the wrong pair.

SOLUTION SCHEME

Make a chart for yourself as follows:

Doctor	Lawyer

Write "Mr. Horton," "wife," "son," or "mother" in each box in as many ways as possible—crossing off any unused boxes—so that no condition is contradicted.

The Two Cubes

Here is a picture of two cubes:

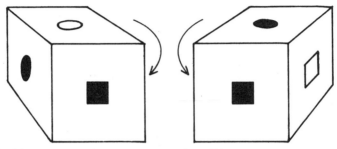

[1] The two cubes are exactly alike.

[2] The hidden faces indicated by the arrows have the same figure on them.

Which figure—○, ●, □, or ■ —is on the faces indicated by the arrows?

Orientation and Solution Scheme, page 36; Solution, page 101.

The Guards

Art, Bob, Cab, and Ida are guards in a museum.

[1] Each of Art, Bob, and Cab stands guard on exactly four days every week.

[2] Exactly two persons stand guard together every day.

[3] No person stands guard three days in a row.

[4] Here is a partial listing that shows when they stand guard every week:

Sun	Mon	Tues	Wed	Thurs	Fri	Sat
Art	Cab	Ida	Art	Bob	Cab	Ida
Bob	?	?	?	?	?	?

Who does not stand guard with Ida?

Orientation and Solution Scheme, page 37; Solution, page 102.

The Two Cubes

ORIENTATION

The two identical cubes may be thought of as one cube in two different positions.

SOLUTION SCHEME

Draw a multiview cube as shown below.

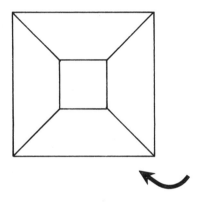

Place ○, ●, □, or ■
on each face of this multiview
cube and at the arrow (to
indicate the only face not seen)
so that no condition is contradicted.

The Guards

ORIENTATION
"Three days in a row" applies to any sequence of three days including (a) Friday, Saturday, and Sunday and (b) Saturday, Sunday, and Monday.

SOLUTION SCHEME

Make a chart for yourself as follows:

	Sun	Mon	Tues	Wed	Thurs	Fri	Sat
On guard	Art	Cab	Ida	Art	Bob	Cab	Ida
	Bob	?	?	?	?	?	?

Write "Art," "Bob," or "Cab" in each column so that no condition is contradicted.

Brothers

Amos, Bert, and Clem are brothers.

[1] Amos has exactly two brothers with grey eyes.

[2] Bert has exactly two brothers with grey or hazel eyes.

[3] Clem has exactly two brothers who do not have blue eyes.

[4] At least one of the three has hazel eyes and at least one of the three has blue eyes.

Whose eyes do you know the color of?

Orientation and Solution
Scheme, page 40;
Solution, page 103.

Equal Products

A   D
B G E
C   F

Each of seven digits from 0, 1, 2, 3, 4, 5, 6, 7, 8, and 9 is:

[1] Represented by a different letter in the figure above.

[2] Positioned in the figure above so that $A \times B \times C$, $B \times G \times E$, and $D \times E \times F$ are equal.

Which digit does G represent?

Orientation and Solution
Scheme, page 41;
Solution, page 104.

Brothers

The total number of brothers is not given.

SOLUTION SCHEME

Make a chart for yourself as follows:

Eye color of

Amos	Bert	Clem

Write "grey," "hazel," or "blue" in each box in as many ways as possible—crossing off any unused boxes—so that no condition is contradicted.

Equal Products

ORIENTATION

A and C are interchangeable, D and F are interchangeable, and each vertical row is interchangeable with the other—but not with the horizontal row; only G can be determined with certainty. Each of A, C, D, F, and G occurs in only one product; each of B and E occurs in two products.

SOLUTION SCHEME

Make a chart for yourself as follows:

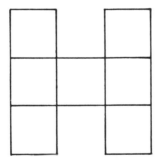

Write a digit in each box so that no condition is contradicted.

The Joker

A total of 21 cards consisting of 4 kings, 4 queens, 4 jacks, 4 tens, 4 nines, and 1 joker were dealt to Alec, Bill, and Carl. Then all jacks, tens, and nines were discarded. At that point:

[1] The combined hands consisted of 4 kings, 4 queens, and 1 joker.
[2] Alec had 2 cards, Bill had 3 cards, and Carl had 4 cards.
[3] The man with the most singletons did not have the joker.
[4] No man had more than 2 kings.

Who had the joker?

Orientation and Solution Scheme, page 44; Solution, page 105.

The Joker

ORIENTATION

A hand contains a singleton when it contains only one king or only one queen or the joker.

SOLUTION SCHEME

Make a chart for yourself as follows:

Alec's hand	Bill's hand	Carl's hand

Cards:
4 kings
4 queens
1 joker

Identify the cards in each person's hand so that no condition is contradicted.

Tees and Els

Of Annette, Bernice, and Cynthia:

[1] Each belongs either to the Tee family whose members always tell the truth or to the El family whose members always lie.

[2] Annette says "Either I belong or Bernice belongs to a different family from the other two."

Whose family do you know the name of?

Solution Scheme, page 46;
Solution, page 104.

Tees and Els

SOLUTION SCHEME

Make a chart for yourself as follows:

If Annette's statement is	Then Annette belongs to the	And then Bernice and Cynthia, respectively, may belong to the
true		
false		

Write "Tee family" or "El family" in each box in the first column and "Tee family" or "El family" in as many ordered pairs as possible in each box in the second column so that no condition is contradicted.

Outre Ornaments

Outre Ornaments, Inc. sells baubles, gewgaws, and trinkets; while there I spoke to three different salespeople.

[1] The first salesperson I talked to told me any 7 baubles together with any 5 gewgaws have the same value as any 6 trinkets.

[2] The second salesperson I talked to told me any 4 baubles together with any 9 trinkets have the same value as any 5 gewgaws.

[3] The third salesperson I talked to told me any 6 trinkets together with any 3 gewgaws have the same value as any 4 baubles.

[4] When I bought some of each kind of ornament I found out exactly one of these salespersons was wrong.

Which salesperson was wrong?

Orientation and Solution
Scheme, page 48;
Solution, page 106.

Outre Ornaments

ORIENTATION

The three value equivalents given must be considered in pairs to determine which one value equivalent is false. The false value equivalent leads to two derived value equivalents that are impossible; the two true value equivalents lead to one derived value equivalent that is not impossible.

SOLUTION SCHEME

Make a chart for yourself as follows:

Conditions	imply				
[1] and [2]		together with		have the same value as	
[2] and [3]					
[3] and [1]					

Complete the table with numbers of baubles, gewgaws, and trinkets.

The Widow

Four women—Anna, Beth, Cass, and Dora—and three men—Earl, Fred, and Gene—play bridge, a card game for four players.

[1] The men and women consist of three married couples and a widow.

[2] The members of each married couple are never partners in a bridge game.

[3] No more than one married couple ever plays in the same bridge game.

[4] One night they played four bridge games in which the partners were as follows:

partners		*partners*
Anna and Earl	versus	Beth and Fred
Anna and Gene	versus	Dora and Fred
Beth and Cass	versus	Fred and Gene
Cass and Earl	versus	Dora and Gene

Who is the widow?

Solution Scheme, page 50;
Solution, page 106.

The Widow

Make a chart for yourself as follows:

	Anna	Beth	Cass	Dora
Earl				
Fred				
Gene				

Place an "X" in each of three boxes to show the three married couples that do not contradict the conditions.

Yes, Yes, Yes

Here is a list of words:

HOE   OAR   PAD   TOE   VAT

[1] Each of three logicians was told one letter of a certain word, so that each logician knew only one of the letters and so that no two logicians knew the same letter.

[2] The logicians were then told their three letters could be arranged to spell one of the words in the list above.

[3] When each logician was asked in turn "Do you know which word the letters spell?," first one logician answered "Yes," then another logician answered "Yes," and then the remaining logician answered "Yes."

Which word did the letters spell?

*Orientation and Solution
Scheme, page 52;
Solution, page 107.*

Yes, Yes, Yes

ORIENTATION

The second logician used the first logician's answer to the question to answer the question, and the third logician used the first and second logicians' answers to the question to answer the question.

SOLUTION SCHEME

Make a chart for yourself as follows:

	A	D	E	H	O	P	R	T	V
The first logician's letter may be									
The second logician's letter may be									
The third logician's letter may be									

Put a check in any column that contains a possible letter each logician may have been told—first in the top row, then in the middle row, and then in the bottom row—so that no condition is contradicted.

Hint: The first logician's letter could not be E since this would contradict [3].

Speaking of Children

"We—Aaron, Brian, and Clyde—each have some children.

[1] Aaron has at least one girl and twice as many boys as girls.

[2] Brian has at least one girl and three times as many boys as girls.

[3] Clyde has at least one girl and three more boys than girls.

[4] When I tell you the number of children we have altogether—a number less than 25—you will know how many children I have, but not how many children each of the others has. Altogether we have . . ."

Who is the speaker?

Orientation and Solution Scheme, page 54; Solution, page 108.

Speaking of Children

ORIENTATION
Some trial and error is necessary in solving this puzzle.

SOLUTION SCHEME
Make a chart for yourself as follows:

Total number of children: _____
Possible numbers of children had by:

Aaron	Brian	Clyde

Write a number in the blank and three numbers in each row of the table in as many ways as possible—crossing off any unused boxes—so that no condition is contradicted.

Mrs. Larchmont's Chair

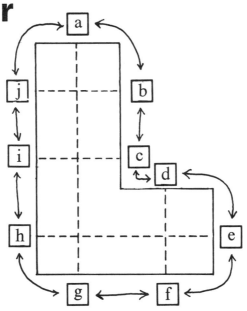

Mrs. and Mr. Larchmont invited four married couples to a dinner party. For the party, chairs were placed around an L-shaped table as shown in the diagram.

Mrs. Larchmont arranged the seating so that:

[1] Every woman sat next to her husband. (Chairs at the ends of a two-headed arrow are "next to" each other.)

(*continued*)

[2] Every woman sat directly across from a man. (Chairs at the ends of a dashed line are "directly across from" each other.)

[3] Mrs. Larchmont sat to the right of Mr. Larchmont.

[4] Mrs. Larchmont was the only woman who did not sit next to a woman.

In which chair—a, b, c, d, e, f, g, h, i, or j—did Mrs. Larchmont sit?

Solution Scheme, page 58;
Solution, page 109.

Card Games

Althea, Blythe, and Cheryl played some card games, each game having exactly one winner.

[1] No player won two games in succession.

[2] When a player was the dealer for a game she did not win that game.

[3] The deal proceeded from Althea to Blythe to Cheryl; then this order was repeated until they stopped playing.

[4] The only player to win more than two games did not win the first game.

Who was the only player to win more than two games?

Solution Scheme, page 59;
Solution, page 109.

Mrs. Larchmont's Chair

SOLUTION SCHEME

Make a diagram for yourself as follows:

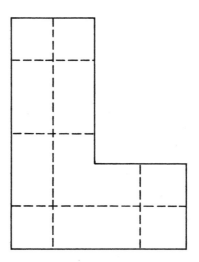

Write "X-1," "Y-1," "X-2," "Y-2," "X-3," "Y-3," "X-4," "Y-4," "X-5," or "Y-5" at each position of the table (X represents one sex, Y represents the other sex, and identical numbers indicate marriage to each other) and locate Mrs. Larchmont's chair so that no condition is contradicted.

Card Games

Make a chart for yourself as follows:

Dealer	A	B	C	A	B	C	A	B	C
Winner									

Using A, B, and C for the women, write a letter in each box —crossing off any unused boxes—so that no condition is contradicted.

Meeting Day

Lou, Moe, and Ned were at the Heave Health Club on the same day this month; it was there and then that they met.

[1] Lou, Moe, and Ned each began going to the health club last month.

[2] One of them goes every 2 days, another one goes every 3 days, and the remaining one goes every 7 days.

[3] Lou went to the health club for the first time this month on a Monday, Moe went to the health club for the first time this month on a Wednesday, and Ned went to the health club for the first time this month on a Friday.

On which day of this month did Lou, Moe, and Ned meet?

Orientation and Solution Scheme, page 62; Solution, page 110.

Meeting Day

ORIENTATION

"Day of this month" is a number from 1 through 31.

SOLUTION SCHEME

Make a chart for yourself as follows:

Health-club attendance dates this month

Lou's dates	
Moe's dates	
Ned's dates	

Write the days of this month each went to the health club so that no condition is contradicted and so that one date occurs three times.

The Tournament

Mr. and Mrs. Aye and Mr. and Mrs. Bee competed in a chess tournament. Of the three games played:

[1] In only the first game were the two players married to each other.

[2] The men won two games and the women won one game.

[3] The Ayes won more games than the Bees.

[4] Anyone who lost a game did not play a subsequent game.

Who did not lose a game?

Solution Scheme, page 64;
Solution, page 111.

The Tournament

SOLUTION SCHEME

Make a chart for yourself as follows:

	Winner	Loser
First game		
Second game		
Third game		

Write "Mr. Aye," "Mrs. Aye," "Mr. Bee," or "Mrs. Bee" in each box so that no condition is contradicted.

Long Word

A certain word has thirteen letters.

[1] Each pair of letters below consists of one letter contained in the word and one "other" letter.

A	B	C	D	E	F	G	H	I	J	L	S	Y
V	W	Q	M	K	U	N	P	O	R	X	T	Z

[2] When the letters in the word are put in the proper order and each "other" letter is put beneath each letter in the word, the "other" letters will appear in alphabetical order.

[3] The word has the same number of letters in common with each of the following words:

FACE   QUEST   QUICK   SWITCH   WORLD

What is the word?

Orientation and Solution Scheme, page 66; Solution, page 112.

Long Word

ORIENTATION

Note that if Q is not the last letter in a word, it must be followed by U.

SOLUTION SCHEME

Make a chart for yourself as follows:

Ordered letters of word												
"Other" letters												

Write one letter in each box so that no condition is contradicted.

Dressing Rooms

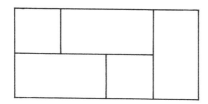

Vera, one of the performers in a play, was murdered in her dressing room. The following facts refer to the dressing rooms shown above. Each of the five performers in the play —Vera, Adam, Babe, Clay, and Dawn—had his or her own dressing room.

[1] The killer's dressing room and Vera's dressing room border on the same number of rooms.

[2] Vera's dressing room borders on Adam's dressing room and on Babe's dressing room.

[3] Clay's dressing room and Dawn's dressing room are the same size.

[4] Babe's dressing room does not border on Clay's dressing room.

Who killed Vera?

Solution Scheme, page 68;
Solution, page 114.

Dressing Rooms

SOLUTION SCHEME

Make a chart for yourself as follows:

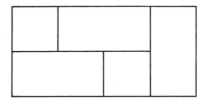

Assign each performer his or her dressing room by writing either "Adam," "Babe," "Clay," "Dawn," or "Vera" in each box so that no condition is contradicted.

Fathers and Sons

Statement A:
Both fathers always tell the truth or both fathers always lie.

Statement B:
One son always tells the truth and one son always lies.

Statement C:
Statement A and statement B are not both lies.

Of the statements above and the men who made them:

[1] Gregory made one of the statements, his father made another of the statements, and his son made the remaining statement.

[2] Each father and son mentioned in the statements refers to one of the three men.

[3] Each man either always tells the truth or always lies.

Which statement—A, B, or C—was made by Gregory?

Orientation and Solution Scheme, page 70; Solution, page 115.

Fathers and Sons

Gregory is the only one of the three who is both a father and a son.

SOLUTION SCHEME

Make a chart for yourself as follows:

Statement A	
Statement B	
Statement C	

Write "true" or "false" for each statement so that no condition is contradicted and so that the truth or falseness of each man's statement is not contradicted.

Crossing the Lake

Agnes, Becky, Cindy, and Delia crossed a lake in a canoe that held only two persons.

[1] The canoe held two persons on each of three forward trips across the lake and one person on each of two return trips.

[2] Agnes was unable to paddle when someone else was in the canoe with her.

(continued)

[3] Becky was unable to paddle when anyone else except Cindy was in the canoe with her.

[4] Each person paddled continuously for at least one trip.

Who paddled twice?

Orientation and Solution Scheme, page 74; Solution, page 116.

The Judge's Wife

A	1	G	7	M	13	S	19	Y	25
B	2	H	8	N	14	T	20	Z	26
C	3	I	9	O	15	U	21		
D	4	J	10	P	16	V	22		
E	5	K	11	Q	17	W	23		
F	6	L	12	R	18	X	24		

Edwin is a judge and a numerologist. He is married to a woman whose name:

[1] Has a "product" that is the same as that for JUDGE; using the correspondence of letters and numbers above, this product is $10 \times 21 \times 4 \times 7 \times 5$.

[2] Has no letter in common with JUDGE.
(To find a woman whose name satisfied the conditions above in relation to EDWIN would have been impossible.)

[3] Has no third letter of the alphabet because 3 is his unlucky number.

[4] Has its letters in alphabetical order when the first letter and the second letter are interchanged.

What is the name of the judge's wife?

*Orientation and Solution
Scheme, page 75;
Solution, page 117.*

Crossing the Lake

ORIENTATION

The situation is analogous to this simpler situation: P, Q, R, and S wish to cross a lake in a canoe that holds only two persons. So (1) P paddles Q across, (2) P paddles back, (3) P paddles R across, (4) P paddles back, (5) P paddles S across.

SOLUTION SCHEME

Make a chart for yourself as follows:

Paddler

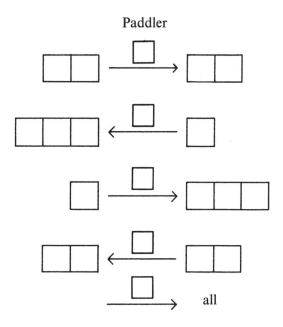

Using A, B, C, and D for the women write a letter in each box to show the paddler and the outcome of each crossing so that no condition is contradicted.

The Judge's Wife

ORIENTATION

It is not necessary to multiply the numbers to solve this puzzle; in fact, it is a good idea not to. This puzzle involves a knowledge of women's first names.

SOLUTION SCHEME

Make a chart for yourself as follows:

$$10 \times 21 \times 4 \times 7 \times 5 = \underline{\quad} \times \underline{\quad} \times \underline{\quad} \times \underline{\quad} \times \underline{\quad} \times \underline{\quad} \times \underline{\quad} \times \underline{\quad} \times \underline{\quad} \times \underline{\quad}$$

Write one number in each blank—crossing off any unused blanks and ×s—to indicate letters that do not contradict the conditions.

Arguments

One of four people—two men, Aubrey and Burton, and two women, Carrie and Denise—was murdered. The following facts refer to the people mentioned.

[1] Aubrey's sister argued exactly once with Carrie's legal husband after the murder.

[2] Burton's sister argued twice with the victim's legal spouse after the murder.

Who was the victim?

Orientation and Solution
Scheme, page 78;
Solution, page 118.

The Three Piles

Three piles of chips—pile I consists of one chip, pile II consists of two chips, and pile III consists of three chips—are to be used in a game played by Amelia and Beulah. The game requires:

[1] That each player in turn take only one chip or all chips from just one pile.

[2] That the player who has to take the last chip loses.

[3] That Amelia now have her turn.

From which pile should Amelia draw in order to win?

Orientation and Solution Scheme, page 79; Solution, page 119.

Arguments

ORIENTATION

After the murder the victim could not have argued with anybody.

SOLUTION SCHEME

Make a chart for yourself as follows:

Aubrey's sister	Carrie's husband		Burton's sister	Victim's spouse

Write "Aubrey," "Burton," "Carrie," or "Denise" in each box so that no condition is contradicted.

The Three Piles

Amelia must draw from one of the piles so that, after Beulah makes any allowed draw, Amelia may draw to win eventually; on her second draw Amelia must draw so that, after Beulah makes any allowed draw, Amelia may draw to win eventually; etc. If Amelia doesn't make the one right draw each time it is her turn, Beulah gets to be in the winning position.

SOLUTION SCHEME

Make a chart for yourself as follows:

	Possible game o oo ooo	Possible game o oo ooo	Possible game o oo ooo
Amelia goes	_ __ ___	_ __ ___	_ __ ___
Beulah goes	_ __ ___	_ __ ___	_ __ ___
Amelia goes	_ __ ___	_ __ ___	_ __ ___
Beulah goes	_ __ ___	_ __ ___	_ __ ___
Amelia goes	_ __ ___	_ __ ___	_ __ ___
Beulah goes	_ __ ___	_ __ ___	_ __ ___

Show the chips remaining after each allowed draw so that, after any allowed draw by Beulah, Amelia can always compel Beulah to take the last chip. (Cross off any unnecessary "pile" lines.)

The Line-Up

Four men—Abraham, Barrett, Clinton, and Douglas —are standing in a line-up.

[1] One man is fair, handsome, and unscarred.

[2] Two men who are not fair are each standing next to Abraham.

[3] Barrett is the only man standing next to exactly one handsome man.

[4] Clinton is the only man not standing next to exactly one scarred man.

Who is fair, handsome, and unscarred?

Orientation and Solution Scheme, page 82; Solution, page 120.

Sum Word

```
    N O S I E R
  + A S T R A L
  ─────────────
    7 2 5 6 1 3
```

In the addition above, the sum represents a word.

[1] Each letter represents a different digit.

[2] No letter represents zero.

What word is represented by 7 2 5 6 1 3?

Orientation and Solution Scheme, page 83; Solution, page 122.

The Line-Up

ORIENTATION

The men are standing in some order such as A B C D or
C A D B. Certain orders are equivalent: for example A B C D
is equivalent to D C B A; if an onlooker sees the backs of the
four men while another onlooker sees their faces, the situation
remains unchanged even though the order is reversed for one
onlooker.

SOLUTION SCHEME

Make a chart for yourself as follows:

Fair?				
Handsome?				
Scarred?				

Write "A" (Abraham), "B" (Barrett), "C" (Clinton), and
"D" (Douglas) in some order along the top of the chart and
write "yes" or "no" in each box below so that no condition
is contradicted.

Sum Word

ORIENTATION

Nine different letters occur in the addition, each one representing a digit other than zero (1, 2, 3, 4, 5, 6, 7, 8, and 9). Some trial and error is necessary in solving this puzzle, but the trial and error can be minimized by first considering the left two columns.

SOLUTION SCHEME

Make a chart for yourself as follows:

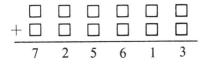

Write a digit in each box—to discover its corresponding letter—so that no condition is contradicted.

The Exam

Five students—Adele, Betty, Carol, Doris, and Ellen—answered five questions on an exam consisting of two multiple-choice (a, b, or c) questions and three true-or-false (t or f) questions.

[1] They answered the questions as follows:

	I	II	III	IV	V
Adele	a	a	t	t	t
Betty	b	b	t	f	t
Carol	a	b	t	t	f
Doris	b	c	t	t	f
Ellen	c	a	f	t	t

[2] No two students got the same number of correct answers.

Who got the most correct answers?

Orientation and Solution
Scheme, page 86;
Solution, page 123.

Sitting Ducks

Mr. and Mrs. Astor, Mr. and Mrs. Blake, Mr. and Mrs. Crane, and Mr. and Mrs. Davis were seated around a table as shown at right. At the table:

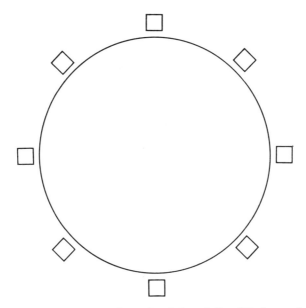

[1] Mrs. Astor was insulted by Mr. Blake who sat next to her on her left.

[2] Mr. Blake was insulted by Mrs. Crane who sat opposite him across the center of the table.

[3] Mrs. Crane was insulted by the hostess who was the only person to sit next to each one of a married couple.

[4] The hostess was insulted by the only person to sit next to each one of two men.

Who insulted the hostess?

Orientation and Solution Scheme, page 87; Solution, page 125.

The Exam

ORIENTATION

Each student has at least one true or false answer in common with every other student; knowledge of this fact eliminates much trial and error in determining the score of each student. Consideration of the total number of correct answers also eliminates much trial and error.

SOLUTION SCHEME

Make a chart for yourself as follows:

	I	II	III	IV	V
Adele	a	a	t	t	t
Betty	b	b	t	f	t
Carol	a	b	t	t	f
Doris	b	c	t	t	f
Ellen	c	a	f	t	t

Circle the correct answer to each question so that no condition is contradicted.

Sitting Ducks

ORIENTATION

The people are arranged around the table in such a way that two men are separated by one person and the members of a married couple are separated by one woman.

SOLUTION SCHEME

Make a chart for yourself as follows:

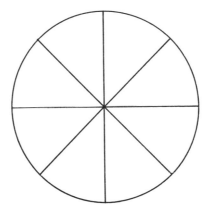

Using the symbols M-A for Astor man, W-A for Astor woman, etc., place the Astors, Blakes, Cranes, and Davises around the table so that no condition is contradicted.

The High Suit

Wilson, Xavier, Yoeman, and Zenger were playing a card game in which three cards from each player's holding remained to be played and in which one of four *suits*—clubs, diamonds, hearts, spades—was the *high suit*. The play of four cards, one from each player's holding, was a *trick*; the suit of the card played first in a trick was the *suit led*.

[1] The distribution of the four suits on the cards held by the four players was as follows:

Wilson's holding — club   heart   diamond
Xavier's holding — club   spade   spade
Yoeman's holding— club   heart   heart
Zenger's holding — spade   diamond   diamond

[2a] A player had to play a card in the suit led, if possible, at each trick.

[2b] If he could not do [2a], he had to play a card in the high suit, if possible.

[2c] If he could not do [2b], he could play any card.

[3]   Each of the remaining three tricks contained in part: the suit card led, just one other card in the same suit, and a card in the high suit which won the trick.

[4] A player who won a trick had to lead at the next trick.

Which suit was the high suit?

Orientation and Solution Scheme, page 90; Solution, page 127.

The High Suit

ORIENTATION

The high suit is equivalent to the trump suit used in the play of many card games.

SOLUTION SCHEME

Make a chart for yourself as follows:

Remaining tricks	Wilson's holding	Xavier's holding	Yoeman's holding	Zenger's holding
First				
Second				
Third				

Write "C" (club), "D" (diamond), "H" (heart), or "S" (spade) in each box so that no condition is contradicted. Hint:

C	S	H	S
H	C	H	D
D	S	C	D

contradicts [2b] because clubs would be high suit (from [3]) and Yoeman's holding as given in [1] shows Yoeman would have played a heart at the first trick to a spade lead (from [3]); and contradicts [4] because clubs would be high suit and diamonds would be led at the third trick (from [3]).

Solutions

The Fight

From [1], Charles is not the older fighter. From [3], Bernard is not the younger fighter. So either:

Case I. Anthony is the older fighter and Charles is the younger fighter.

Case II. Bernard is the older fighter and Anthony is the younger fighter.

Case III. Bernard is the older fighter and Charles is the younger fighter.

Then:

From [3], Charles is the taller fighter for Case I and Charles is taller than Anthony for Case III.

From [1], Bernard is the shorter fighter for Case II and Bernard is shorter than Anthony for Case III.

From [1] and [3], Charles is taller than Bernard for Case III.

In summary:

	Older fighter	Younger fighter	Taller fighter	Shorter fighter
Case I	Anthony	Charles	Charles	Anthony
Case II	Bernard	Anthony	Anthony	Bernard
Case III	Bernard	Charles	Charles	Bernard

(Note that this reasoning eliminates nine of the twelve cases mentioned in the Discussion without considering what those nine cases are.)

From [2], Anthony is not the shorter fighter; so Case I is eliminated. From [2], Bernard cannot be both older and shorter than Charles; so Case III is eliminated. Then Case II is the correct one and *Charles is not fighting*.

Then, from [2], Bernard is younger than Charles (so Charles is the oldest of the three and Anthony is the youngest) and, from [3], Anthony is taller than Charles (so Anthony is the tallest of the three).

My Secret Word

From the "clue": If you were told any one of the letters in MOD, then you would not be able to determine whether the number of vowels in my secret word is one or two. So none of the letters in MOD is in my secret word. Then my secret word cannot be AIM, DUE, MOD, or OAT. So *my secret word is TIE.*

The Tennis Players

From [1], the players must be relatively positioned in one of the following ways:

daughter	son	daughter	Zita
brother	Zita	brother	son
Ia		Ib	

son	daughter	Zita	daughter
Zita	brother	son	brother
IIa		IIb	

Then, from [2]:	
For ways Ia and IIa	For ways Ib and IIb
Brother is the worst player's sibling.	Daughter is the worst player's sibling.
Zita is the worst player.	Son is the worst player.

Then, from [3]:	
For ways Ia and IIa	For ways Ib and IIb
Brother is the best player.	Brother is the best player.

So, in any case, *Zita's brother is the best player.*

After-Dinner Drink

From [1] and [2] there are six possibilities:

	Abigail orders	Bridget orders	Claudia orders
Case I	coffee	coffee	coffee
Case II	coffee	tea	tea
Case III	tea	coffee	coffee
Case IV	tea	tea	tea
Case V	tea	coffee	tea
Case VI	tea	tea	coffee

Then, from [3], Cases I and V are eliminated and, from [4], Cases II and V are eliminated. So you know *Abigail always orders the same drink* (tea) *after dinner.*

Equal Sums

One digit must be 9. Then, from [1] and [2], 9 must go with 1 and 3. One digit must be 8. Then, from [1] and [2], 8 must go with either·1 and 4 or 2 and 3. One digit must be 7. Then, from [1] and [2], 7 must go with either 1 and 5 or 2 and 4. One digit must be 6. Then, from [1] and [2], 6 must go with either 2 and 5 or 3 and 4.

From the diagram no digit may be used in more than two sums. From this and the fact that 9 goes with 1 and 3:

Case I. If 8 goes with 1 and 4, then 7 goes with 2 and 4; then 6 goes with 2 and 5.

Case II. If 8 goes with 2 and 3, then 6 goes with 2 and 5; then 7 goes with 1 and 5.

But Case II is impossible because the digit 4 does not occur. So Case I is correct and, from the diagram, *E must be 4.*

A possible arrangement of the digits is shown below.

$$9 \; 3 \; 1$$
$$8$$
$$4 \; 7 \; 2$$
$$5$$
$$6$$

Relations

From [1]:

If Lee's spouse is Dale, then Dale's sibling cannot be Lee and must be Terry; then Terry's sister-in-law cannot be Dale and must be Lee.

If Lee's spouse is Terry, then Terry's sister-in-law cannot

be Lee and must be Dale; then Dale's sibling cannot be Terry and must be Lee.

Then, in any case, all three of Lee, Dale, and Terry are accounted for and Terry's sister-in-law is a female.

So, from [2], Lee's spouse and Dale's sibling are both males. In summary:

	Lee's spouse	Dale's sibling	Terry's sister-in-law
	male	male	female
Case I	Dale	Terry	Lee
Case II	Terry	Lee	Dale

Case II is eliminated because Lee and Terry cannot both be males and married to each other. So Case I is the correct one and you know *Dale is a married man.* Lee is a married woman, Dale and Terry are brothers, and Lee is Terry's sister-in-law.

1	2	3
4	5	6
7	8	9

X and O

Let a number in each square as shown indicate the location of a mark. Then, from [3], the seventh mark must be placed in square 5 and, from [2], the seventh mark wins for both X and O. So the sixth mark must have been placed in a line already containing two of the opponent's marks—in either square 7 or square 9; otherwise, either X or O would have been placed in square 5. But, from [3], the sixth mark could not have been placed in square 7 because square 5 would have been the required location for the O in square 7. So the sixth mark was placed in square 9 and was X. Then, from [1], the seventh mark will be O and, from [2], *O wins the game.*

From previous reasoning, the fifth mark placed in the game can also be determined: O in square 8.

Names

From [1] and [4], Miss Alden, Miss Brent, and Miss Clark are named Fay. From [1], no one can have more than two of the names; so, from [1] and [2], Kay is distributed only twice with Fay in one of two ways:

Case I   Alden   Brent   Clark   Doyle   Evans

                   Fay   Fay   Fay
                   Kay   Kay

Case II   Alden   Brent   Clark   Doyle   Evans

                   Fay   Fay   Fay
                           Kay   Kay

Then, from [1] and [3], neither Miss Brent nor Miss Clark is named Gay in either case. So—from [1]—Miss Alden, Miss Doyle, and Miss Evans are named Gay. Then Case I is impossible and Case II becomes:

Case II   Alden   Brent   Clark   Doyle   Evans

                   Fay   Fay   Fay
                           Kay   Kay
                   Gay   Gay   Gay

Then, from [1], Miss Evans is named Fay. Then, from [1], *Miss Brent is named May.*

Hockey Scores

From [1] and [3]: The team that lost the greatest number of games lost the two games it played (there were three losers and the teams could not have each lost one game). So the team that lost the greatest number of games did not score 6 and did not score 5 and 4 together. The highest total of two scores achieved by this team is greater than the total of at least 7 (6 and at least 1) achieved by some other team. So this team scored 5 and 3 for a total of 8.

Then the 5 score lost to the 6 score and the 3 score lost to the 4 score. So the 1 score and the 2 score go together and the 6 and the 1 were scored by the same team. Let the teams be X, Y, and Z temporarily; then in summary:

Z	Y		X	Y		X	Z
1	2		3	4		5	6

From inspection of the team scores, any two higher scores differ by at least one and at most two; any two lower scores differ by at least one and at most two. So, from [2], the Angoras' higher score and the Bobcats' higher score differ by two and the Bobcats' lower score and the Cougars' lower score differ by one. So the Angoras must be Z, the Bobcats must be Y, and the Cougars must be X. Then *the Cougars achieved the highest total of its two scores.*

The Journey

From [3]: No two of the L-shaped fields are the same kind of field; these can be assigned letters, such as east-E, west-W, and south-S, to represent either corn, wheat, or rye. Then E, W, and S can be assigned to the fields surrounding them by alternating W and S around the east L-shaped field, alternating E and S around the west L-shaped field, and alternating E and W around the south L-shaped field. Then 1 is a W field, 5 is an E field, and 12 is an S field.

1W		4	5 E
2 E	3 S	W	6 S
W		east	
west		E	10W
		south	
7	8	9	S
S	E	W	11 E	12 S

From [1] and [2] and inspection of the plan, the only possible route involves fields 6-S, 4-W, 3-S, west L-shaped, south L-shaped, 10-W, and 12-S. So, from [2], each E field is a rye field and *the east L-shaped field is a rye field.*

The Visits

From [1] and any of [2], [3], and [4], at least one woman visited Edna in the morning and at least one woman visited Edna in the evening. From [3], Alma did not visit Edna first. So, from [1], the order of the visits must be one of the following:

Case I.   Bess (9), Alma (8), Cleo (10), Dina (11)
Case II. Bess (9), Cleo (10), Alma (8), Dina (11)
Case III. Bess (9), Cleo (10), Dina (11), Alma (8)
Case IV. Bess (9), Dina (11), Alma (8), Cleo (10)
Case V.   Cleo (10), Alma (8), Bess (9), Dina (11)
Case VI. Cleo (10), Dina (11), Alma (8), Bess (9)
Case VII. Dina (11), Alma (8), Bess (9), Cleo (10)

From [2], Cases I, V, VI, and VII are eliminated. Then, from [4], Cases II and III are eliminated. So Case IV is the right one and *Cleo visited Edna last.*

A Different Age

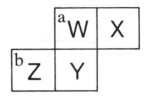

Let W, X, Y, and Z represent the four digits as shown in the diagram. Then, from [1] and [2], Ambrose's age is a two-digit number and WX plus Brandon's age equals WY. So Brandon's age must be a one-digit number.

From [3], WY plus Chester's age equals ZY. So Chester's age must end in zero. Then Chester's age must be a two-digit number.

From [4] and the fact that only Brandon's age is a one-digit number, *Brandon is a different age in years from the other two.*

Because Chester's age ends in zero, Ambrose's age must end in zero. So Ambrose and Chester may each be 10, 20, 30, or 40 and Brandon may be 1, 2, 3, 4, 5, 6, 7, 8, or 9. Of the thirty-six possible ways to complete the diagram, here is one:

The Doctor and the Lawyer

The two women are not blood relatives. So, from [2], if the doctor is a woman, the lawyer is a man. Then, from [3], the doctor is a man. Because a contradiction arises from assuming the doctor is a woman, the doctor must be a man.

Mr. Horton's son is the youngest of the four and is a blood relative of each of the other three. So, from [1], the doctor is not Mr. Horton's son. Then *you know the occupation of Mr. Horton: he is the doctor.*

From [1], then, the lawyer cannot be Mr. Horton's mother. So the lawyer is either his wife or his son. (The doctor may be older than the lawyer.) Then *you don't know the occupation of anyone else.*

The Two Cubes

From [1] and the pictured cubes, at least one of ● and ◼ occurs twice.

If both occur twice, then the identical cubes look like:

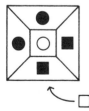 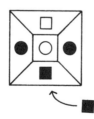 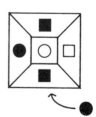

But in each case duplicate faces cannot occur at the arrows, contradicting [2].

So either only ● occurs twice or only ◼ occurs twice.

If only ● occurs twice, then the identical cubes look like this:

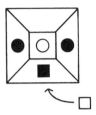

But in this case duplicate faces cannot occur at the arrows, contradicting [2].

So only ■ occurs twice and the identical cubes look like this:

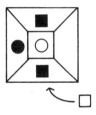

In this case the ○ occurs on the right cube at the arrow. So, from [2], the ○ occurs on the left cube at the arrow. Thus ○ *is on the faces indicated by the arrows.* (The ○ occurs on the unmarked face in the last diagram.)

The Guards

From [1] and [2], Ida stands guard on only two days each week. Then in [4] Ida is not one of the unknown guards and either Bob (Case I) or Cab (Case II) stands guard with Art on Wednesday.

So, using this information and [3] to complete [4] in each case:

Case I. If Bob stands guard on Wednesday, then Art stands guard on Friday. Then Cab stands guard on Thursday and Bob stands guard on Saturday. Then Art stands guard on Monday. Then Cab stands guard on Tuesday.

Case II. If Cab stands guard on Wednesday, then Art stands guard on Thursday. Then Bob stands guard on Tuesday and Friday. Then Art stands guard on Monday. Then Cab stands guard on Saturday.

In either case, *Art does not stand guard with Ida.*

Brothers

From [4], six cases are possible:

	Eye color of Amos	Eye color of Bert	Eye color of Clem
Case I	hazel	blue	
Case II	hazel		blue
Case III	blue	hazel	
Case IV		hazel	blue
Case V	blue		hazel
Case VI		blue	hazel

From [1], then, a fourth brother has grey eyes in each case. Then: from [1] and [2], Cases I and VI are impossible; from [1] and [3], Cases II and IV are impossible; from [1] and [3], Clem has grey eyes in Case III; and, from [1] and [2], Bert has grey eyes in Case V.

So *you know only the color of Amos' eyes: they are blue.* (Any more than four brothers must also have blue eyes, from [3].)

Equal Products

From [1] and [2]: No letter can be 0, 5, or 7. The product for each row, then, is a multiple of 1, 2, 3, 4, 6, 8, and 9. So the smallest possible product is 8×9 or 72 and the product is a multiple of 72. But the product cannot be any of 72×2, 72×3, etc. because it is not possible to get a product larger than 72 three times. So the product is 72.

Then:

$$72 = \boxed{1 \times 8 \times 9} = 2 \times 36$$
$$= \boxed{2 \times 4 \times 9} = 3 \times 24$$
$$= \boxed{3 \times 4 \times 6}$$

Because 4 and 9 are used twice (see boxed products), B or E is 4 and the other is 9. So *G is 2.*

A possible arrangement of digits is:

$$\begin{array}{ccc} 6 & & 8 \\ 4 & 2 & 9 \\ 3 & & 1 \end{array}$$

Tees and Els

From [1] and [2]:

Case I. If Annette's statement is true, all three cannot be members of the Tee family and Cynthia cannot be the only one of the three who is a member of the El family. So, if Annette's statement is true, either: Annette is the only one of the three who is a member of the Tee family or Bernice is the only one of the three who is a member of the El family.

Case II. If Annette's statement is false, Annette cannot be the only one of the three who is a member of the El family and Bernice cannot be the only one of the three who is a member of the Tee family. So, if Annette's statement is false, either: Cynthia is the only one of the three who is a member of the Tee family or all three are members of the El family.

Then: Annette is a member of the Tee family in Case I and Annette is a member of the El family in Case II. Bernice is a member of the El family in Case I and Bernice is a member of the El family in Case II. Cynthia may be a member of either family in Case I and Cynthia may be a member of either family in Case II. So *you know only the name of Bernice's family* (El).

The Joker

From [1] and [3], one man had exactly two singletons: a king and a queen. From [2], Bill cannot have had exactly two singletons. From [1] and [2], Carl cannot have had exactly two singletons unless one of them was the joker. So Alec had the singleton king and the singleton queen.

Then, from [3], each of Bill and Carl cannot have had more than one singleton. If Carl had no singletons, then—from Alec's holding and [1] and [2]—he had two kings and two queens. But then, from [1] and [2], Bill would have had three singletons—contradicting previous reasoning. So Carl had exactly one singleton.

Then—from [1], [2], and [4]—Carl had three queens and a singleton king; if Carl had the joker instead of a singleton king, Bill would have had three kings—contradicting [4]. Then, from the other men's holdings and from [1] and [2], *Bill had the joker* and two kings.

Outre Ornaments

Let b represent baubles, g represent gewgaws, t represent trinkets, + represent "together with," and = represent "have the same value as." Using [2], substitute 4b+9t for 5g in [1]. Using [3], substitute 6t+3g for 4b in [2]. Using [1], substitute 7b+5g for 6t in [3]. Then simplify. In summary:

	Using [2]		Simplify	
[1] 7b+5g=6t	⟶	7b+4b+9t=6t	⟶	11b+9t=6t

	Using [3]		Simplify	
[2] 4b+9t=5g	⟶	6t+3g+9t=5g	⟶	15t+3g=5g

	Using [1]		Simplify	
[3] 6t+3g=4b	⟶	7b+5g+3g=4b	⟶	7b+8g=4b

[1], using [2], is impossible because some baubles and 9 trinkets cannot have the same value as 6 trinkets. [3], using [1], is impossible because some gewgaws and 7 baubles cannot have the same value as 4 baubles. Because only one salesperson was wrong, from [4], neither the second nor the third salesperson was wrong; otherwise, more than one salesperson was wrong. So only *the first salesperson was wrong.*

One possible price list, from [2] and [3], is:

    trinket—$ .80
    bauble—$5.70
    gewgaw—$6.00

The Widow

From [1], [2], and [4]:

    Either Fred is married to Anna or Fred is married to Cass.
    If Fred is married to Anna, then Gene is married to Beth or Gene is married to Cass.

If Gene is married to Beth, then Earl is married to Dora.

If Gene is married to Cass, then Earl is married to Beth or Earl is married to Dora.

If Fred is married to Cass, then Gene is married to Beth; then Earl is married to Dora.

In summary, the married couples are either:

Case I	Case II	Case III	Case IV
Fred-Anna	Fred-Anna*	Fred-Anna	Fred-Cass*
Gene-Beth or	Gene-Cass or	Gene-Cass* or	Gene-Beth*
Earl-Dora	Earl-Beth*	Earl-Dora*	Earl-Dora

From [3] and [4], Cases II, III, and IV are impossible (asterisks show two couples in one game). So Case I is the correct one and, from [1], *Cass is the widow.*

Yes, Yes, Yes

From [1], [2], and [3]: The first logician to answer "Yes" must have been told a letter that occurred only once in the list. So the first logician was told either H, R, P, D, or V. Then the second logician knew the first logician was told either H, R, P, D, or V. So the second logician knew the word was not TOE. Then the second logician knew what the word was if told T or E (some new letter), or if told the second letter of PAD that occurred only once in the list: P or D. The third logician knew the first logician was told either H, R, P, D, or V and knew the second logician was told either T, E, P, or D. So the third logician knew the word was not OAR. So the third logician knew what the word was if told O (some new letter), but would not know what the word was if told A. Then, rather than PAD or VAT, *the letters spelled HOE.*

Speaking of Children

From [1], Aaron has at least 3 children and a number of children from this sequence:

3, 6, 9, 12, 15, 18, 21, 24, . . .

From [2], Brian has at least 4 children and a number of children from this sequence:

4, 8, 12, 16, 20, 24, . . .

From [3], Clyde has at least 5 children and a number of children from this sequence:

5, 7, 9, 11, 13, 15, 17, 19, 21, 23, . . .

Then the total number of children is at least 12 and, from [4], at most 24. Also: If the total number of children is even, Aaron must have an odd number of children; if the total number of children is odd, Aaron must have an even number of children.

Trial and error reveals the following information. The total number of children cannot be 13 because no three numbers, one from each sequence, can total 13. The total cannot be 12, 14, 15, 16, or 17 because then the number of children each had would be known, contradicting [4]. The total cannot be 18, 20, 21, 22, 23, or 24 because then no number of children could be known for anybody, contradicting [4]. So the total is 19.

When the total is 19 Aaron must have an even number of children and, from the sequences, this number must not be greater than 19–(4+5) or 10. So Aaron must have 6 children. Then Brian and Clyde together must have 13 children. Then Brian must have either 4 or 8 children. Then: If Brian has 4 children, Clyde has 9 children; if Brian has 8 children, Clyde has 5 children.

So *the speaker is Aaron.*

Mrs. Larchmont's Chair

Let X represent one sex, let Y represent the other sex, and place an X in chair a.

Then, from [1], the spouse of the person in chair a is either in chair b—Case I—or in chair j—Case II. Conditions [1] and [2] can be used alternately to determine the couples (X-1 and Y-1, X-2 and Y-2, etc.) in each case, by beginning at chair a and following the arrows:

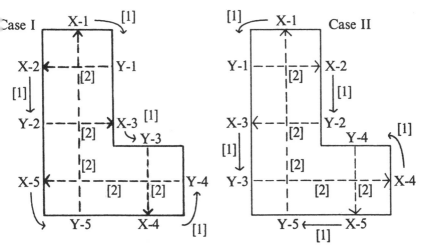

In Case I, three members of each sex did not sit next to a member of the same sex; so, from [4], Case I is eliminated. Then Case II is the correct case.

Then, from [4], Mrs. Larchmont sat in either chair i or chair j. Then, from [3], *Mrs. Larchmont sat in chair j.*

Card Games

Let A represent Althea, B represent Blythe, and C represent Cheryl. Then, from [1] and [2], the possible sequence of wins is as follows:

Dealers, from [3]	A	B	C	A	B	C	A	B
Case I	C*	A	B	C	A	B	C	–
Case II	B	A*	B	C	A	B	–	–
Case III	B	C	B*	C	A	B	–	–
Case IV	B	C	A	C*	A	B	C	–
Case V	B	C	A	B	A*	B	–	–
Case VI	B	C	A	B	C	B*	–	–
Case VII	B	C	A	B	C	A	C*	–
Case VIII	B	C	A	B	C	A	B	–

From [4], listing continues until one player wins three games. (Each asterisk indicates the point where the rest of a sequence is determined; one deal earlier a choice between two players is possible. Each succeeding case represents the other choice for the preceding case.) From [4], Cases I, II, III, V, VI, and VIII are eliminated. So Case IV or VII is the right one. In either case, *Cheryl was the only player to win more than two games.*

Meeting Day

From [1] and [2], the two-day man went to the health club for the first time this month on the 1st or the 2nd and the three-day man went to the health club for the first time this month on the 1st, 2nd, or 3rd. Then, from [3], the two-day man went on the 1st and the three-day man went on the 3rd. Then—from [1], [2], and [3]—the seven-day man went to the health club for the first time this month on either the 5th or the 6th. In summary, either A or B below is true.

A. Lou went on Monday, the 1st, and every two days thereafter; Moe went on Wednesday, the 3rd, and every three days thereafter; and Ned went on Friday, the 5th, and every seven days thereafter.

B. Moe went on Wednesday, the 1st, and every two days thereafter; Ned went on Friday, the 3rd, and every three days thereafter; and Lou went on Monday, the 6th, and every seven days thereafter.

The dates for A and B, then, are as follows (the dates in parentheses depend upon the length of the month):

A. Lou's dates—1, 3, 5, 7, 9, 11, 13, 15, 17, 19, 21, 23, 25, 27, (29), (31)
   Moe's dates—3, 6, 9, 12, 15, 18, 21, 24, 27, (30)
   Ned's dates—5, 12, 19, 26

B. Moe's dates—1, 3, 5, 7, 9, 11, 13, 15, 17, 19, 21, 23, 25, 27, (29), (31)
   Ned's dates—3, 6, 9, 12, 15, 18, 21, 24, 27, (30)
   Lou's dates—6, 13, 20, 27

Because the three men were at the health club on the same day this month, possibility A is eliminated. So possibility B is correct. Possibility B reveals that *Lou, Moe, and Ned met on the 27th of this month.*

The Tournament

From [2] and [3], either:

I. Mr. Aye won one game, Mrs. Aye won one game, and Mr. Bee won one game; or
II. Mr. Aye won two games and Mrs. Aye won one game; or
III. Mr. Aye won two games and Mrs. Bee won one game.

If I is correct, then: From [1] and [4], Mr. Bee beat Mrs. Bee in the first game. Then, from [4], only Mr. Bee could have lost to Mr. Aye or Mrs. Aye in the second game. Then, from [1] and [4], no one could have played against the last winner in the last game. So I is not correct.

II cannot be correct from [1] and [4].

So III is correct. If Mrs. Bee won the first game, then she beat Mr. Bee in that game, from [1]. But then, from [1] and [4], no one could have played against Mr. Aye in the second game. So Mr. Aye won the first game against Mrs. Aye, from [1]. Then, from [4], Mr. Aye beat Mr. Bee in the second game. Then, from [4], Mrs. Bee beat Mr. Aye in the third game.

So *only Mrs. Bee did not lose a game.*

Long Word

From [3], the number of common letters is at most four. From [1] and QUEST in [3], the number of common letters is at least one—S or T. From [1], from FACE and QUEST in [3], and from the fact that Q cannot occur in the thirteen-letter word without U:

	If the number of common letters is	then each of these loops contains a common letter	then each of these loops contains a common letter
(i)	4	Ⓠ Ⓤ Ⓔ [S T C F K [T S]	F A C Ⓔ Ⓤ V Ⓠ K
(ii)	1	Q U E [S T Ⓒ Ⓕ Ⓚ [T S]	Ⓕ A Ⓒ E U V Q Ⓚ
(iii)	2	Q Ⓤ E [S T Ⓒ F Ⓚ [T S]	F A Ⓒ E Ⓤ V Q Ⓚ
(iv)	2	Q U Ⓔ [S T Ⓒ Ⓕ K [T S]	Ⓕ A Ⓒ Ⓔ U V Q K

or

(v)	3	Q̲U̲ E ⌈S T⌉ C F K̲ ⌊T S⌋	F A C E U̲ V Q̲K̲
		or	
(vi)	3	Q U̲E̲ ⌈S T⌉ C̲ F K ⌊T S⌋	F A C̲E̲ U̲ V Q K

A contradiction occurs in (i), (ii), (iv), and (v), so these are eliminated.

Then, from (iii) and (vi), A is a common letter.

Then, from [1] and from QUICK in [3]:

	If each of these loops contains a common letter	then each of these loops contains a common letter	Possible?
(iii)	Q U̲ E ⌈S T⌉ F A̲C̲ E C̲ F K̲ ⌊T S⌋ U̲ V Q̲K̲	Q U̲ I C̲K̲ C̲ F O Q E	no
(vi)	Q U̲E̲ ⌈S T⌉ F A̲C̲E̲ C̲ F K ⌊T S⌋ U̲ V Q K	Q U̲ I C̲ K C̲ F O Q E̲	yes

Then I is the third common letter in QUICK.

Then, from [1] and [3], the common letters in SWITCH are I, C, and S/T. Then, from [1] and [3], the common letters in WORLD are not W and not O (because I is common); so the common letters in WORLD are R, L, and D.

Ten of the thirteen letters are now known: C, U, E, A, I, R, L, D, P (not H), and B (not W). So, from [1] and [2], twenty-four letters can be arranged thus (the pairs S/T and Y/Z can only go where indicated):

UP RE D I C S A B L Y
F H J K M O Q T V W X Z

It is now easy to see that: the letters in the pair G/N should be reversed and placed after the pair U/F, the letters in the pair S/T should be reversed, and *the word is UNPREDICTABLY.*

Dressing Rooms

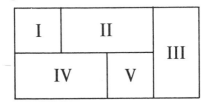

From [4], neither Babe nor Clay occupies dressing room II; from [1], Vera does not occupy dressing room II. So either Adam or Dawn occupies dressing room II.

Suppose Adam occupies dressing room II; then, from [3], one of the following sets of occupation must exist (A represents Adam, C represents Clay, and D represents Dawn):

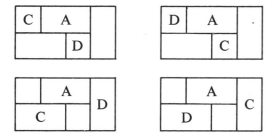

But, from [2], each of these sets of occupation is impossible.

So Dawn occupies dressing room II. Then, from [3], one of the following sets of occupation must exist:

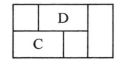
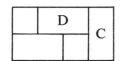

But, from [2], the first of these sets is impossible. So the second set is the correct one and, from [2], Vera occupies dressing room IV.

Then, from [4], Babe occupies dressing room I. So Adam occupies dressing room V.

Then, from [1], *Adam killed Vera.*

Fathers and Sons

If statement C is false, statement A and statement B are both false. But—from [1], [2], and [3]—if statement A is false, statement B or statement C is true (because a false statement A implies one father always tells the truth and one father always lies). So statement C cannot be false and must be true.

Because statement C is true, at least one of statements A and B is true. But—from [1] and [2]—if statement B is true, statement A or statement C is false. So if statement B is true, statement A is false.

In summary:

	Case I	Case II
Statement A	true	false
Statement B	false	true
Statement C	true	true

If Case I were the right one, then—from statement A and from [2]—the speakers of statements A and C would both be fathers; and—from statement B and from [2] and [3]—the speakers of statements A and C would both be sons (because a false statement B implies both sons always tell the truth or both sons always lie). This situation is impossible from [1] because only Gregory is both a father and a son; so Case I is eliminated.

Then Case II is the right one. Then, from statement A and

from [2] and [3], the speaker of statement A is a father; and, from statement B and from [2], the speaker of statement A is a son. So, from [1], *Gregory made statement A*.

Crossing the Lake

From [1], [2], and [4], Agnes paddled on at least one return trip.

The person who paddled twice did not paddle on two forward trips because, from [1], she would then have had to paddle on a return trip, contradicting [4]. So the person who paddled twice paddled on at least one return trip.

In summary, Agnes and the person who paddled twice each paddled on at least one return trip. So Becky, Cindy, and Delia each paddled on one forward trip, from [1] and [4].

Then, from [1] and [3], Cindy was in the canoe when Becky paddled on a forward trip. Because Cindy was in the canoe on two forward trips, she must have paddled on a return trip. So *Cindy paddled twice*.

Six paddling sequences are possible. To determine an actual sequence of paddlings, Celia's (C) and Agnes' (A) paddlings are listed first, then Becky's (B) paddling, and then Delia's (D) paddling. The sequences are shown below.

C	D	D
BD ——→ AC	BC ——→AD	BC ——→AD
A	A	A
ABD ←—— C	ABC ←—— D	ABC ←—— D
D	C	B
B ——→ACD	B ——→ ACD	A ——→BCD
C	C	C
BC ←—— AD	BC ←—— AD	AC ←—— BD
B	B	C
——→all	——→all	——→all

C	B	B
BD ——→ AC	AD ——→ BC	AD ——→ BC
C	C	C
BCD ←—— A	ACD ←—— B	ACD ←—— B
B	C	D
D ——→ ABC	D ——→ ABC	C ——→ ABD
A	A	A
AD ←—— BC	AD ←—— BC	AC ←—— BD
D	D	C
——→ all	——→ all	——→ all

The Judge's Wife

From [1], the name of the judge's wife has a "product" of

$$10 \times 21 \times 4 \times 7 \times 5.$$

From [2], her name has no G(7) or U(21); so it has N(14) twice. Division by 14 twice leaves $10 \times 3 \times 5$.

$$
\begin{array}{r|l}
14 & 10 \times 21 \times 4 \times 7 \times 5 \\
\hline
14 & 10 \times 21 \times 2 \times 5 \\
\hline
& 10 \times 3 \times 5
\end{array}
$$

From [2], her name has no E(5) or J(10). It cannot have a T(20). It cannot have an I(15); otherwise, it would have an E(5) or a J(10). So her name has a Y(25). Division by 25 leaves 2×3.

$$
\begin{array}{r|l}
25 & 10 \times 3 \times 5 \\
\hline
& 2 \times 3
\end{array}
$$

From [3], her name has an F(6). Division by 6 leaves 1.

$$
\begin{array}{r|l}
6 & 2 \times 3 \\
\hline
& 1
\end{array}
$$

In alphabetical order the letters found so far are FNNY and the only other letter her name may contain is A(1). So, from [4], *the name of the judge's wife is FANNY.*

(The W in Edwin is the twenty-third letter of the alphabet and can only be represented as 23×1. So to find a woman whose name satisfied the first two conditions in relation to EDWIN is impossible.)

Arguments

From [1], Aubrey's sister is either Carrie or Denise.

Suppose Aubrey's sister is Carrie. Then, from [1], Carrie's husband is Burton. Then, from [1] and [2], Burton's sister is Denise.

Suppose Aubrey's sister is Denise. Then, from [1], Carrie's husband is either Aubrey or Burton. Suppose Carrie's husband is Aubrey; then, from [2], Burton's sister can be either Carrie or Denise. Suppose Carrie's husband is Burton; then, from [1] and [2], Burton's sister is Denise.

In summary:

| | Arguers in [1] | | Arguers in [2] | |
	Aubrey's sister	Carrie's husband	Burton's sister	Victim's spouse
Case I.	Carrie	Burton	Denise	?
Case IIa.	Denise	Aubrey	Carrie	?
Case IIb.	Denise	Aubrey	Denise	?
Case IIc.	Denise	Burton	Denise	?

In Case I, Aubrey must be the victim. Then the victim's legal spouse can only be Denise. This situation is impossible, so Case I is eliminated.

In Case IIb, either Burton or Carrie must be the victim. If Burton is the victim, then Burton can have no legal spouse;

this situation contradicts [2]. If Carrie is the victim, then Denise and Aubrey argued exactly once—from [1]—and twice—from [2]; this situation is impossible. So Case IIb is eliminated.

In Case IIc, either Aubrey or Carrie must be the victim. If Aubrey is the victim, then Aubrey can have no legal spouse; this situation contradicts [2]. If Carrie is the victim, then Denise and Burton argued exactly once—from [1]—and twice—from [2]; this situation is impossible. So Case IIc is eliminated.

Then Case IIa is the correct one. Then *Burton must be the victim*. From [2], Burton's spouse can only be Denise.

The Three Piles

In the chart below:

For the first four opening moves by Amelia, only winning moves by Beulah are given for any moves by Amelia after the opening.

For the last opening move by Amelia, any moves by Beulah are given for only winning moves by Amelia.

When two piles have the same number of chips, a removal of some chips from one pile is equivalent to a removal of the same number of chips from the other pile.

From [1] and [3]:	Amelia takes pile III	Amelia takes pile II
From [1]: { Amelia goes / Beulah goes / Amelia goes	O OO ___ O ___ ___ ___ ___ ___	O ___ OOO O ___ ___ ___ ___ ___
From [2]:	Amelia loses	Amelia loses

119

From [1] and [3]:	Amelia takes pile I	Amelia takes one chip from pile III
From [1]: Amelia goes	___ ○○ ○○○	○ ○○ ○○
Beulah goes	___ ○○ ○○	___ ○○ ○○
Amelia goes	___ ○ ○○	___ ○○ ___
Beulah goes	___ ○ ___	___ ○ ___
Amelia goes	___ ___ ___	___ ___ ___
From [2]:	Amelia loses	Amelia loses

From [1] and [3]:	Amelia takes one chip from pile II		
From [1]: Amelia goes	○ ○ ○○○	○ ○ ○○○	○ ○ ○○○
Beulah goes	___ ○ ○○○	○ ○ ○○	○ ○ ___
Amelia goes	___ ○ ___	○ ○ ○	___ ○ ___
Beulah goes	___ ___ ___	___ ○ ○	___ ___ ___
Amelia goes	___ ___ ___	___ ○ ___	___ ___ ___
Beulah goes	___ ___ ___	___ ___ ___	___ ___ ___
From [2]:	Amelia wins	Amelia wins	Amelia wins

So *Amelia should draw one chip from pile II in order to win.*

The Line-Up

From [2] (A represents Abraham and ? represents an unknown man):

Fair ? |? |A| ?|
        |no| |no|

So, from [1], either:

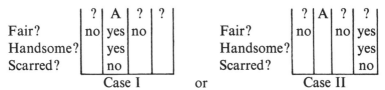

	?	A	?	?
Fair?	no	yes	no	
Handsome?		yes		
Scarred?		no		

Case I

or

	?	A	?	?
Fair?	no		no	yes
Handsome?				yes
Scarred?				no

Case II

Each of two scarred men cannot be standing next to Clinton in either Case I or Case II. So, from [4], Clinton is standing next to no scarred man and each of the other men is standing next to exactly one scarred man. Then either (C represents Clinton):

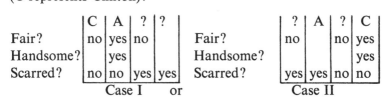

	C	A	?	?
Fair?	no	yes	no	
Handsome?		yes		
Scarred?	no	no	yes	yes

Case I

or

	?	A	?	C
Fair?	no		no	yes
Handsome?				yes
Scarred?	yes	yes	no	no

Case II

In Case I, Clinton is standing next to exactly one handsome man. So, from [3], Case I is impossible.

Then Case II is the correct one and *only Clinton is fair, handsome, and unscarred.*

In Case II, the man next to Clinton cannot be handsome, from [3]. Then, from [3], the man on the other end from Clinton cannot be handsome. If Abraham is handsome, Barrett is on the other end (from [3]). If Abraham is not handsome, Barrett is standing next to Clinton (from [3]). So either (B represents Barrett and D represents Douglas):

	B	A	D	C
Fair?	no		no	yes
Handsome?	no	yes	no	yes
Scarred?	yes	yes	no	no

Case IIa

or

	D	A	B	C
Fair?	no		no	yes
Handsome?	no	no	no	yes
Scarred?	yes	yes	no	no

Case IIb

Abraham may be either fair or not fair.

Sum Word

N+A cannot be 7; otherwise, O and S are both 1 which contradicts [1] or one of O and S is zero which contradicts [2]. So N+A is 6 and 1 is carried from O+S. Then, from [1] and [2], the possible digits for N and A are as follows:

N	5	1	4	2
A	1	5	2	4

Then R+L cannot be 3; otherwise, R and L are 3 and 0 which contradicts [2] or 1 and 2 which contradicts [1]. So R+L is 13.

Then E+A is 10.

So, choosing values for R and L from [1], the table can be continued:

	i	ii	iii	iv	v	vi	vii
N	5	5	1	4	4	2	2
A	1	1	5	2	2	4	4
E	9	9	–	8	8	6	6
L	7	6		7	6	8	5
R	6	7		6	7	5	8

Case iii is eliminated from [1].

Then R+I is 15 and not 5, from [2]. So, from [2], Case vi is eliminated and, from [1], Cases i and v are eliminated.

Then continuing the table:

	ii	iv	vii
N	5	4	2
A	1	2	4
E	9	8	6
L	6	7	5
R	7	6	8
I	8	9	7

Then S+T is 4 and not 14, from [1]. So, from [1] and [2], Case ii is eliminated and O+S is 12. Then continuing the table:

	iv	iv	vii	vii
N	4	4	2	2
A	2	2	4	4
E	8	8	6	6
L	7	7	5	5
R	6	6	8	8
I	9	9	7	7
T	3	1	3	1
S	1	3	1	3
O	–	–	–	9

Case iv is eliminated from [1].

So Case vii is the correct one. Substituting the letters for the digits, *7 2 5 6 1 3 is I N L E T S.*

The Exam

From [1], each student has at least one true-false answer in common with every other student. So if one student got five correct answers, then each student got at least one correct answer. Then, from [2], the number of correct answers must total 1+2+3+4+5 or 15. Because the maximum number of correct answers is 2 (a or b) +2 (a or b) +4 (t) +4 (t) +3 (t) or 15, from [1], Adele's answers would have to be the five correct ones. But then Betty and Doris would each have exactly two correct answers, and Carol and Ellen would each have exactly three correct answers, contradicting [2]. So no one got five correct answers.

Then, from [2], the number of correct answers must total 0+1+2+3+4 or 10. Then the student who got none correct cannot be Adele, Carol, or Doris because the total number of correct answers cannot be the required 10 when the correct answers for III and IV are both f; because each f occurs only once, the maximum total possible would be 9. So Betty or Ellen got none correct.

If Betty got none correct, then the correct answers for the true-false questions would be: III. f (occurs once), IV. t (occurs four times), and V. f (occurs twice). Then Carol, Doris, and Ellen would each have at least two correct answers; so Adele would have to be the student with one correct answer: IV. t (occurs four times). Adele's and Betty's multiple-choice answers would, then, be incorrect; so the correct multiple-choice answers would have to be: I. c (occurs once) and II. c (occurs once). But, then, the total number of correct answers would not be the required 10: 1 (c) $+1$ (c) $+1$ (f) $+4$ (t) $+2$ (f) $=9$. So it is Ellen and not Betty who got no correct answers.

Because Ellen got none correct, the correct answers for the true-false questions must be: III. t (occurs four times), IV. f (occurs once), and V. f (occurs twice). Then Betty, Carol, and Doris each got at least two correct answers; so Adele got one correct answer: III. t (occurs four times). Then Adele's and Ellen's multiple-choice answers are incorrect; so the correct multiple-choice answer for I is b (occurs twice); so, because the total number of correct answers is 10, the correct multiple-choice answer for II must be c (occurs once).

In summary, the correct answers in order are: b, c, t, f, f and are shown below in circles.

	I	II	III	IV	V
Adele	a	a	(t)	t	t
Betty	(b)	b	(t)	(f)	t
Carol	a	b	(t)	t	(f)
Doris	(b)	(c)	(t)	t	(f)
Ellen	c	a	f	t	t

So *Doris got the most correct answers.*

Sitting Ducks

From [4], the partial seating arrangement of men and women around the table was either (M represents man and W represents woman):

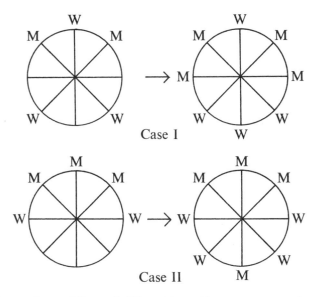

Case I

Case II

Then, from [1] and [2], either (A represents Astor, B represents Blake, and C represents Crane):

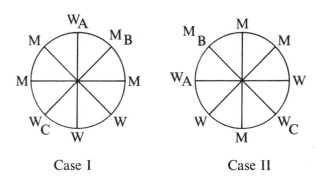

Case I   Case II

From [3], no man sat next to each one of a married couple; so, in Case I, Mrs. Blake sat opposite Mrs. Astor. But, then, no woman can sit next to each one of a married couple as required by [3]; so Case I is eliminated.

Then Case II is the correct case. Then Mrs. Blake and Mrs. Davis were seated in one of the following ways (D represents Davis):

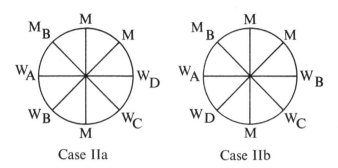

Case IIa   Case IIb

Then, in Case IIa, Mrs. Astor is the hostess who was the only person to sit next to each one of a married couple. But either Mr. Astor or Mr. Davis has to be one of the men sitting opposite each other, so that more than one person sat next to each one of a married couple. This situation contradicts [3]; so Case IIa is eliminated.

Then Case IIb is the correct case. Then Mrs. Blake or Mrs. Davis must be the hostess, from [3]. If Mrs. Blake is the hostess, then Mr. Crane sat next to her. Then Mr. Astor has to be one of the men sitting opposite each other, so that more than one person sat next to each one of a married couple. This situation contradicts [3]; so Mrs. Davis is the hostess.

Then, from [3], Mr. Astor sat next to Mrs. Davis while Mr. Davis sat next to Mrs. Blake. So Mr. Crane sat opposite Mr. Astor.

So, from [4], *Mr. Crane insulted the hostess.*

The High Suit

From [1] and [3], three different suits were led and the high suit was not led.

From [1], [2], and [3]:

(i) Clubs were not led first.

(iia) If diamonds were led first, neither clubs nor diamonds is the high suit.

(iiia) If spades were led first, neither clubs nor hearts nor spades is the high suit.

(iva) If hearts were led first, neither spades nor hearts is the high suit.

Then—from [1], [3], and [4] and from (iia), (iiia), and (iva) respectively:

(iib) If diamonds were led first, a club was led second.

(iiib) If spades were led first, a heart or a club was led second.

(ivb) If hearts were led first, a spade was led second.

The deductions above produce six possibilities as shown in the table below (C represents clubs, D represents diamonds, H represents hearts, S represents spades, and a circled letter represents the high suit):

	I	II	III	IV	V	VI
Trick	Suits	Suits	Suits	Suits	Suits	Suits
First	D D (S)	D D (H)	S S (D)	S S (D)	H H (C)	H H (D)
Second	C C (S)	C C (H)	H H (D)	C C (D)	S S (C)	S S (D)
Third	H H (S)	S S (H)	C C (D)	H H (D)	D D (C)	C C (D)

Case I is eliminated because no one could have won the second trick with a spade and led a heart. Case II is eliminated because no one could have won the second trick with a heart and led a spade. Case V is eliminated because Xavier would have led the

127

spade and both Wilson and Yoeman would have had to play a club. So, in any case, *diamonds was the high suit.*

Cases III and IV are eliminated because only Wilson could have led at the second trick after winning the first trick and only Wilson could have led at the third trick after winning the second trick, an impossible situation. Case VI is the only one possible, yielding two ways in which the fourth cards could have been played from the holdings; see below (W represents Wilson's holding, X represents Xavier's holding, etc.).

Trick	Holdings			
	W	X	Y	Z
First	H	C	H	Ⓓ
Second	Ⓓ	S	H	S
Third	C	S	C	Ⓓ

Trick	Holdings			
	W	X	Y	Z
First	H	S	H	Ⓓ
Second	Ⓓ	S	C	S
Third	C	C	H	Ⓓ

Index (solution pages in italics)